THE PENGUIN
COLONEL PEWTER

Born in Melbourne, Australia, Arthur Horner
trained at the National Art School, Sydney and
the Central School of Arts and Crafts, London.
He was a cartoonist for the *Bulletin* and *Smith's
Weekly* before the war but moved to London in
1946 where he worked for *Tribune*, the *News
Chronicle*, *New Statesman* and *Punch*.

His first Colonel Pewter story was published in
1952 in the English *News Chronicle*. The stories
ran for eighteen years in English newspapers
and in the Melbourne *Age*.

Arthur Horner returned to Australia in 1976 and
now draws regularly for the *Age*, including 'The
Uriel Report'.

THE PENGUIN
COLONEL PEWTER

THREE WHIMSHIRE STORIES BY ARTHUR HORNER

Greenfingers

Outward Ho!

Special Attraction

Penguin Books Ltd,
Harmondsworth, Middlesex, England
Penguin Books,
625 Madison Avenue, New York, N.Y. 10022, U.S.A.
Penguin Books Australia Ltd,
Ringwood, Victoria, Australia
Penguin Books Canada Ltd,
2801 John Street, Markham, Ontario, Canada
Penguin Books (N.Z.) Ltd,
182-190 Wairau Road, Auckland 10, New Zealand

Greenfingers first published in the *Guardian*, London and the *Age*, Melbourne 1965
Outward Ho! first published in the *Guardian*, London and the *Age*, Melbourne 1966
Special Attraction first published in the *Guardian*, London and the *Age*, Melbourne 1967

This collection first published 1978
Copyright © Arthur Horner, 1965, 1966, 1967, 1978
Made and printed in Hong Kong

Horner, Arthur
The Penguin Colonel Pewter

ISBN 0 14 70074 9
1. Comic books, strips, etc. –
Australia. 2. Australian wit and
humor, pictorial. I. Title

741.59'94

GREENFINGERS

or, SEEDS OF REVOLT...

THE STORY OF SOMETHING RUM THAT HAPPENED IN COLONEL PEWTER'S CONSERVATORY, AND ITS EFFECT ON THE PARISHIONERS OF ST. VITUS'S...

OUR STORY BEGINS DOWN IN WHIMSHIRE, IN COLONEL PEWTER'S CONSERVATORY...

Hmm....let's see now....Giant Harbinger ...Improved Perfection ...how's this, Glub?

Deathless Queen: New Season's novelty — delicately curved... pale-fleshed...peerless purity...succulent—

It's a very pretty picture—

M'no, it doesn't do to mess about with strange seeds — we'd best stick to last year's reliable old drumhead—

Uncle— you're not ready!

You haven't forgotten what tonight is—after you promised to take me!

Eh?...Of course not, boy—it's—um... you tell him, Glub—

Of course I haven't forgotten, it's — let me see now — the Quirk Boy Scouts' All Star Variety Extravaganza in the Memorial Hall —

No, no — we went to that last week —

Then it's the — don't tell me — the Great Tittering Thespian Society's panto, Mother Goose —

No, no, Uncle — it's Mr. Chumble's Lecture at the Church Hall!..

You promised to come — 'n' I have to go cos Mr. Chumble is relying on me to work the Magic Lantern!..

Pomme-soul, yes — the seed order will have to wait, Glub — get the motor out...

Poor Mr. Chumble...

AND SOON: I hope the Rector gets a better turnout than he does on Sundays — even at his last Harvest Festival I counted more heads amongst the cabbages than the congregation

AT ST. VITUS'S CHURCH HALL THE RECTOR IS ALL SET TO GIVE HIS LECTURE...

My dear friends, I am very — um — happy tonight to be able to — um — give you an — um — illustrated report on my recent sojourn with our Mission in the — um — Wayward Isles...

Well, it's how they come in the box, Mr. Chumble —

No, no boy — that can't be it —

AND AFTER ONE OR TWO FALSE STARTS...

Gad!

...AND A QUICK RESHUFFLE

Oh dear — it's always the same when I lend things to the Bishop...

— THE LANTERN SLIDES GET UNDER WAY...

Ah, yes — now here we see a typical Wayward Islander — um — male, that is...

I think the seed catalogue would've given us a more exciting evening than this looks like being, Glub —

5 Well, that concludes my –um– little talk, dear friends, but I have here a number of –um– souvenirs which you may care to look at more closely while refreshments are being –um– prepared...

Here – keep an eye on your cat, boy – don't know why you have to take her everywhere –

Chloe's all right, Uncle – just curious, that's all –

TOTEM OBJECT (Recent)

What's this, Padre?

Oh, that is a carved gourd – the dried fruit of the –um– yumyum tree –

– a tree believed by the Wayward Islanders to have –um– magic properties – these superstitions, you know...

6 What does this magic yumyum tree look like, Mr. Chumble?

Alas, my boy, there were none to see – apparently the jungles there were once full of them, but the –um– natives had such frequent resort to them and were such poor husbandmen they let them die out years ago –

Now nothing remains but a few ancient –um– dried gourds which they regard as –um– sacred relics...

How'd you come by this one, Padre?

It was given me by a grateful convert – to show he had put away such nonsense...

I say! this rattles – must be seeds inside –

RATTLE

Oops! – Butterfingers!

You see, what the Bishop says is true — I'm afraid the congregations have rather — um — dwindled away ...

The process was — um — accelerated in my absence abroad by the well-meaning efforts of my — um — curate, young Tom Skene —

Jesus loves me! Yeah-yeah—

ST. VITUS'S
TODAY:
BIKE BLESSING SUNDAY
EVENSONG:
JOE BLOW &
THE JERICHOS
THE SMASH HITTITES

SCREECH!

— In endeavouring to — um — widen the appeal of the services he unfortunately alienated the — um — older worshippers without gaining the permanent support of the — um — younger —

So I'm afraid a Petition of indignant parishioners would not be worth the — um — postcard its written on ...

Hmmm...

Look, I'll get my lawyer on to this — old Beedle might ferret out some legal stick to beat 'em with —

Thank you, Colonel — I'm not very hopeful, though—

18

And no harm in trying your Petition — tell you what, get that Pinyon woman to organise it — she's a dab at that sort of thing —

That's true.

Well, chin up, Chumble — by the way, I'm hardly one of your faithful — what made you come to me?

Well, my flock are rather a — um — meek lot, and this situation seems to call for a — um — **militant** approach—

Don't worry, Padre — we'll give your Church Commissioners hell! ...

THE COLONEL IS AS GOOD AS HIS WORD...

...There it is in a nutshell, Beedle— what can you do about it?

Hmm—..can't see how we can stop the Church selling their own land—

— As for St Vitus's, it hardly comes into the Preservation Order category... Leave it with me, Colonel, I'll see what can be done

Good man, Beedle— bound to be a fly in their ointment somewhere

Uncle Pewter— Come and see the yumyum tree— it's grown..!

And look!— it's got flowers!

Bless my soul

Look at that, Glub— beats anything in last years show, eh..?

It seems to grow while you watch it—

Best move it outside, Glub— against the front wall, where it'll get the sun—

Oh— and don't dig any more of my special compost in with it— we don't want it to get out of hand...

AND SO A TOUCH OF THE TROPICS COMES TO RURAL WHIMSHIRE---

MAGIC YUMYUM TREE

THE COLONEL'S NEW PLANT ATTRACTS CONSIDERABLE ATTENTION...

Oh-ah-good morning Colonel—I was just admiring your new shrub—most unusual—

It is, rather—its a yumyum—

A magic yumyum—

Pretty tricky thing to grow actually—would you like a cutting..?

Thank you, Colonel-er-some other time perhaps...

AND, AS WORD GETS ROUND, BY GARDENERS' GRAPEVINE...

CHUKKAS NO FAKIRS

AT COPSE COTTAGE, IN NEARBY PUCKERBROW:

Good-um-morning, Mrs Pinyon, I—

Why its you, Mr. Chumble—Come on in—

You're just in time to try a glass of my Parsnip '64—last of the vintage, worse luck—

That is most kind of you—

BONK!

An unpretentious cottage-bottled wine, free of neuroses—ideal for elevenses, don't you think?

It's very-um-palatable.

Especially with one of my organically-grown stone-ground wholemeal fairy cakes—there.... And now, what can I do for you, Rector?

Well, dear lady, I have come to enlist your-um-support...

THE RECTOR HAVING TOLD HIS STORY...

Pull down St. Vitus's?! But that's a *monstrous* idea!!...

We thought a petition might help—Colonel—um—Pewter suggested you would be just the one to organise it—

Well, I *have* had quite a few successes—I remember I once held Lord Terminus's stirrup-cup for him while he signed my anti-hunting petition—'Terminus, MFH—'

Oh, well done!

Just leave it all to me, Rector—and now, you must excuse me—I have a couple of pots in the kiln...

Thank you, Mrs. Pinyon—and for the—um—refreshment—

BONK!

'...We the undersigned, ~~conscious~~ jealous as we are of our cultural ~~heri~~—and spiritual heritage'...

BONK! BONK

Ouch! Deuteronomy 28:19!...

LATER, AT SUPPER-TIME...

How's this, Pinny?... 'We the undersigned, jealous as we are of our cultural and spiritual heritage, protest most strongly at the proposed demolition of the Church of St. Vitus'—

Sounds all right—no wine tonight?

Oh, the Rector polished off the last of the Parsnip '64 at elevenses—

What about the gooseberry ordinaire...?

That went off at Christmas—and the sparkling rhubarb blew up last summer, remember? We're right out, I'm afraid—I'll have to make some more

Do you have to, Fabia? the Green Man does quite a decent rough cider—

It is a *Whimshire* tradition, the making of *vins du pays*—I'm just waiting till I can get some dried fruit that's not South African, that's all—

Oh, all right—I'll have a cup of tea...

LATER, AT 'CHUKKAS'...

Uncle Pewter! Come and see the yumyum tree!

Mmp?.. What now?

Look!— little gourds— forty-three of them— I counted!..

Bless my soul— that's quick—

MAGIC YUMYUM TREE

25

Uncle— if each of these gourds had only two seeds— that would be enough to start up the yumyum forests again—

That's a thought lad...

And the Wayward Islanders could have their magic once more!...

M'yes— whatever that might have been...

BEFORE VERY LONG...

WHEEZE

AREEOWCH!

Uncle! A speckled chit was eating the gourds —and when Chloe chased him he dive-bombed her—!

Birds at the fruit, eh?

I'll show 'em, by jingo!

26

Good morning, Glub — is the Colonel in?

You'll find him out in the garden, Ma'am...

Ah, Colonel — I'm after your signature, for the St. Vitus's petition —

Oh, of course — how's it going — bags of names?

Not many so far, I'm afraid. If the Meek *do* inherit the earth, Chumble's flock will all be v.i.p.'s...

Hello — what's this? — a tree with *fruit* on it?

Oh yes — just thinning 'em out. It's a yumyum actually — grew it from a seed old Chumble brought back — using my own special compost...

29

Yumyum..? Never heard of it — is the fruit edible?

Well, the birds eat it, dammit — and Chumble says the Wayward Islanders set great store by it —

I wonder if I could have some, Colonel — I'm wanting to make some more wine —

By all means — let me fill your basket.

30

Lovely — I say Colonel, what's all this 'magic' yumyum tree?

Oh, that's the boy's label — some nonsense of Chumble's about the natives investing it with magic properties

What fun!... Well, thank you, Colonel — and I'll let you have a bottle of yumyum '65 just as soon as it's ready!...

Oh-ah-please don't trouble Mrs P...

NEXT SUNDAY, AFTER MATINS...

Good to see you here, Colonel — an all too in-frequent-um-visitor

Oh, well, thought I'd best show the flag, time like this—

Damgood fighting sermon of yours. today. Chumble- kept me awake for once—

Ah yes, I felt Exodus could be relied on to meet the present-um-situation...

How's the protest going? Did the Parochial Church Council Meeting produce anything?

Not even a-um-quorum, I'm afraid. And Mrs Pinyon's petition has been most disappointing.

31

I only hope it will impress the -um-Bishop. I have an appointment at the Palace tomorrow—

Well, good luck, Chumble. And - if need be, smite old Quirk hip-&-thigh!...

NEXT MORNING, AT QUIRK PALACE...

It is good of you to see me, my lord —

Come in, Chumble— come in—

A sad business, these redundancies- I hate to see a House of God come down — particularly in my own diocese, Chumble—

My lord, that's what I wanted to—

Still, in the case of St. Vitus's, we are demol-ishing not so much a parish church as a breeding-ground for the pestilential death-watch beetle...

Yes, my lord — but I have come today to -um-ask you—

Come, Chumble, you want to discuss your future benefice -my plans for your preferment, hmm...?

Well — not exactly, my lord—

32

LATER...

Well, Padre, how did the petition go?

I'm afraid the -um-Bishop says it wouldn't be worth submitting even—

Well, that still leaves the legal side—let's go and see what old Beedle has cooked up—

Most—um-kind of you...

MEANWHILE, AT COPSE COTTAGE SOMETHING ELSE IS COOKING...

Let's see, now: Fermentation jar...airlocks... thermometer...hydrometer... yeast—how's the yumyum juice coming along, Pinny?

Almost—pff-ready—

—but I still can't see why it has to be done this—pff-way!

THE COLONEL AND THE RECTOR TAKE ADVICE:

...One takes the Bishop's point that the *smallness* of the Petition tends to invalidate its claim that St. Vitus's fulfils its function as a Parish Church—

How can we stop 'em pulling it down then?

Well, the Union of Benefice Measures do provide that any Member of the public may object to a scheme —and has the right of appeal to the Privy Council—

Good egg—I'll be the objector, then, Beedle—just draft a letter for me and I'll sign it—

I cannot hope to find really valid grounds for objection —but we can delay the demolition for a time—

Well, you never know—something may turn up in the meantime—

AND, AT THIS VERY MOMENT, IN DOCKLAND...

Sposm yufella savvy takim mifella walkabout long place bilong disfella-bilong-Jesus naim Chum Bull..?

Ar-get lost.

nig wog!

37

The Editor, Sir: Your readers will be interested to see the remarkable results I have obtained using a Special Compost of— I say, boy—

♪♪

Going into the garden? Keep an eye on that yumyum, will you?—don't want the birds to get at it—

Right-oh, Uncle—

There's a bird there now, Chloe—look, hopping about underneath the yumyum—

It's found a worm—look at it threshing about like mad—oh! look at *that*!...

SQUAWK!

Golly—I can't believe it, hardly...

Ha! I've been looking everywhere for this spade, Master Martin—

Ssh!... Please don't interrupt, Mr Glub—

We're burying a bird—look, it's a Crested upstart—

Ah, poisoned I expect—

No, I saw it happen! It was hopping round the roots of the yumyum, 'n' I saw it pull out a fat worm—

Too much for it, eh?

It was! Suddenly the worm lashed out with its tail—or its *head*, p'raps—and *bingo!* there was the upstart—dead!...

38

AND NOW SCIENTIFIC ANALYSIS IS ADDED TO LEGAL PARALYSIS...

.... a bit tricky, this — I hope FRED * doesn't get upset...

* Feedback Regenerating Electronic Device

...desire to lodge objection...projected demolition of building of great historic architectural artistic interest...prejudicial effect...pursuant to Town & Country Planning Act, 1947... ad quod damnum...

MRS PINYON BREWS...

'O for a beaker full of the warm South, full of the true, the blushful Hippocrene, With beaded bubbles winking at the'—

Please Fabia, not again!

43

THE RECTOR BROODS...

CLUNK!

Oh dear—that will be the vestry roof—I do believe the beetles will beat the Bishop yet.

Aarr

AND OUR WAYWARD ISLANDER IS STILL ON HIS WAY:

Belly bilong mifella i cry— yu sellum kaikai?

Out!..

RESTAURANT

Missee: Sposm eye bilong yufella stop long disfella paper-yabber—

Cumny closa, ucalla coppa!

Mooch Overdoon? Aarr, yü'm moiles aot— Oi'd best put'ee on booss, Oi rackon...

Sauce o' these immy-grants!.. Ain't safe f'r a girl on the street—

AND SO:

Disfella-bilong-white-queen, i plenty gudfella, olrait!..*

* Your English policemen are wonderful!..

Sposm yu takim mifella longwe longa windwagon, bymby place bilong Chum Bull i come, olrait..?

Much Overdun? Okay, man—

44

What this, man? You takin' the mickey?

Olsem moni tru- mifella sellum boat- aderfella givim plenty moni- no gammon...

Wise guy, huh? Man, you no go shell on this bus- take your- OUCH!

Ha! Liklik fingerfishy!

You go back home, man- this no place for yobboes!

Sposm mifella hab yumyum, makum yu long pig!

Ayayai! Nau ollataim watawata i come—!

MUCH OVERDUN

* Wet season?

MEANWHILE, IN MUCH OVERDUN...

Beedle! You have some news about St Vitus's—

I have, Colonel...

45

I'm afraid the Church Commissioners have turned down your objection as a Member of the Public to the proposed demolition of St Vitus's—

The devil! They have!

46

Then we'll appeal to the Privy Council -get cracking Beedle—

I shouldn't advise that, Colonel- you see, I tried them on all possible counts from the Ancient Monuments Act to the Constitution of Otho of 1237 —

But since the scheme had been cleared beforehand with the Ministry of H.E.L.G. and the Ministry of Works it was a case of sime fibula standare...

Hard cheese! Poor old Chumble, I say! You haven't seen my yumyum have you, Beedle?

WHILE AT COPSE COTTAGE, PUCKERBROW...

There! Five gallons of yumyum '65, crystal clear and ready to drink-almost! You know, Pinny, I shouldn't be surprised if this effort eclipsed my '59 Dandelion!

So long as it doesn't evoke your Cowslip of the year before...

THE RECTOR IS WORKING ON A SERMON...

...For at such a time when our Church is threatened, it behoves us to rise like the Israelites of old and smite the philistines hip and —

Tʒt!... Coomp'ny!

'Tis him wears they bootton-oop kiddi-breeks - nay the Bishop, the oother woon —

You mean the Archdeacon - show him in, Mrs Oddy —

Archdeacon! You have news from the Bishop about St Vitus's..?

I have indeed, Chumble - you will be relieved to know the matter is settled at last —

Certification is completed. — I have called to give you notice that the demolition is set down for next week..

47

Arrangements have been made for the Demolition Contractors to begin work on Monday of next week —

Then - this Sunday will be the last service at St Vitus's —

48

Not quite - the Bishop will attend immediately before demolition begins to conduct a short service of deconsecration: You will make the necessary arrangements—

Of course... So these are my last days at St Vitus's...

Come, Chumble, don't look so glum — you know the Bishop has preferment in mind for you. I believe an incumbency impends at Most Saints, Dorquay...

It's hard to take a man's Church from him—

Of course, if everything does not go smoothly, need I remind you that there are vacant benefices in less salubrious parts— Scragge End, for instance...?

The Bishop may - um - rely on me, of course...

SUNDAY MORNING, AND THE BELLS OF ST. VITUS'S RING OUT —

AND FALL PLEASANTLY ON A DUSKY EAR:

Ai! Belo i Krai! Mi bin fainim misin bilong prista Chum Bull olrait!..

CLANG! CLANG!

Don't turn round, dear! — you don't want to risk having one of your turns during the Service —

Mi lukluk longtaim fainim disfella long paper-tok. Yu tokim mi Kam longwei bilong spike long em...

Eh?.. Rev. Chumble — look here, old chap, this is no time to see the Rector...

MISSION SUNDAY

Look — Rector busy man — no can see you now — it's Sunday!

No can go in there — is Church, savvy.

Olrait, mi wait... Mi longtaim wokabout — no can sindaun nisait..?

MISSION SUNDAY

Well really!

Really! If this is the Rector's idea it's time the Church did close!..

Excuse me! You're blocking the path —

Run along now — chop chop!

Pinny! Did you hear that?

You ought to be ashamed of yourselves! Is Much Overdun to be another Little Rock?!

We friends — you come with us, yes..?

Tenkyu, Misis. Warfoa ologeta man i kros long mi...

AT THE RECTORY, ON THIS SAME SAD DAY...

Aarr, Rev'r'nd — yü'm left yür bitty biled aig oontooched!...

Oh dear! Here come the Demolition Men with their Engines of Destruction!...

BACK AT 'CHUKKAS'...

...So you see, Glub, the yumyum's a bit tricky — we'll have to warn all the people we gave it to — just tell 'em it'll blight their other plants — Let's see, who took cuttings?

Well there was Sir Timothy up at the Hall... Lady Mountescue... old Mrs Robinson... Jack Dibber...

AT COPSE COTTAGE:

Fabia, if you don't hurry I shall miss my train!...

Shan't be a tick — I'm just loading the stuff to drop off at the Church

This ought to do the trick...

AND AT QUIRK PALACE...

Read that bit out again, Kite — I can never remember this Deconsecration business...

Morrnin', Revrrnd — we'm all set tü pull 'er daon...

You can't start yet, my good man!...

— The Church can't be demolished until the Bishop has conducted his Deconsecration Service —

Aarr. Oi hopes'm ain't tü long abaot it, thaatwoise — Oi caan't keep men un machin'ry loyin' oidle, beloike...

Oh, Rector — the Sexton has helped me set out the refreshments in the vestry — it's all set...

Thank you, Mrs Pinyon — I do hope nothing's happened to the Bishop — he's — um — late...

AS IT HAPPENS, ON THE QUIRK BY-PASS:

What are we stopping for?!

Obstruction ahead, my lord

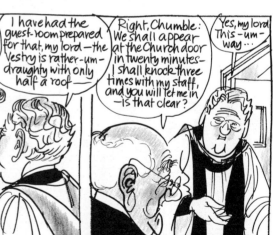

"What about my story?"

"Eh?.. Later, lad, Mrs Pinyon is – ah – not at home for the moment –"

"Rotten old twits! I bet they wouldn't treat a *Fleet Street* reporter like that!.. Hey, I could try Fleet Street with this story myself!..."

"...From Derek Catchpole, our Special Correspondent:..Today the parishioners of the village church of St. Vitus are staging a stay-in strike in defiance of their Bishop, who plans to pull it down... Not since Martin Luther attacked the Archbishop of – hmm, have to look that up in the local library –"

"Aarr.!! *×✱●!!"

WROOMPA!!

AND SOON, AT THE FLEET STREET OFFICE OF THE *DAILY GIMMICK*...

"Well, where's the hot spot this time, Mac – Tokyo?.. Saigon?.. Selma..?"

"Nearer home, Wes, old man – we've had an odd piece phoned in by a would-be stringer down in Whimshire – place called – ah yes Much Overdun..."

AT 'CHUKKAS', THE COLONEL MAKES AN URGENT CALL

"...There it is Gleepers – a whole vestryful of Black Vikings. How long before the stuff fades?"

"Hmm – I'll have to ask FRED – can you hang on for 1/500 sec..?"

"FRED says quote: PIGMENTARY ABERRATION IN HUMAN BEINGS PERSISTS 24 HOURS ± 1 HOUR E & OE. WHOSE FOOL IDEA IS' – Oh, the rest is personal –"

"Right, I'll tell 'em"

MEANWHILE, AT MUCH OVERDUN STATION:

"...Z: Voitu3'3 ?.. Roight be village green, she be – uppen they ain't vetched 'er daon be nao..."

AND SOON:

"Arrahoo Arrayawee! We'll hang the Bishop from our own belfry"

"It's no good knocking – they won't let you in..."

KNOCK KNOCK

"Look, Uncle — TV vans!"

"Well, I did ring the BBC in case they wanted me to do a script—"

"What's this, Hotchkiss? I thought this was an exclusive—!"

"Well here we are on the village green at Much Overdun, scene of the struggle between the Bishop of Quirk and the parishioners of St. Vitus's, just behind me —"

CLANG! CLANG!

"On this side of the green is the village pub, with a number of the villagers sunning themselves outside. Let's see what they think about this clash..."

81

"You, sir, what d'you think of all this?"

"I think it's a pity you lot have to shove your great microphones where they're not wanted!..."

"You can see feelings run deep in this old-world village...and now, what says our genial mine host?"

"Well, it's a pretty tatty old church, you know. I always say the only thing keeps it up whenever a jet flies over must be the death-watch beetles linking arms! Ha ha ha ha ha—!"

82

"And you, sir — have you a comment?"

"Gin goompers blaw i' moogwort toime, Be dummel zens i' thicky roime—"

"Aarr, devinitely..."

"If you want my opinion, I think Chumble is putting up a terrific show, and he and his team should be able to hold out as long as the stuff lasts — I mean, the stuff of true British pluck—"

"Thank you, gentlemen—"

"Well, there's a cross-section of village opinion — now let's move over to the church and hear what the besieged Rector and his followers have to say..."

CLANG! CLANG!

Hello there! Will you open up, please – its the BBC...

Ah – may we come in?

I'm afraid not – but the Rector authorises me to say that he intends to stay in here till the Bishop returns – or at least for 24 hours –

Well, there it is, viewers: Will this village church come down, victim of crumbling fabric and apathy – or will this eleventh-hour militancy of its parishioners save it..?

It will be interesting to see what happens when the Bishop appears tomorrow, to knock once again on this door...

Kite! Turn that off..!!

THAT EVENING! TELEPHONE LINES ARE BUSY – AT PUCKERBROW:

Fabia! What were you doing on TV? – you can't mean to stay the night locked in the vestry..?!

Now, don't worry, Pinny – you'll find some free-grazing pork sausages in the fridge with a plate of organically grown mashed –

– IN THE SNUG AT THE CORNPOPPLE...

Upchat: Siege of St Vitus's – latest: As the night wears on I can see the lights still blazing defiantly from the stained-glass windows of the beshieg-beshiezh – of the doomed church...

IN A FLEET STREET OFFICE –

Mac, this piece of Upchat's – Page One lead with 8 col. banner!... yeah, great stuff... it's got everything – religion, violence, money, sex – by the way, get Wesley to find out the vital stats. of the rector's girl friend, this Pinyon dame – and about the money, I've got a great idea –

WHILE ON THE BBC SWITCHBOARD...

I'm sorry – the switchboard's been jammed ever since that OB from Whimshire –

SCENE: THE QUIRK MAGISTRATES' COURT, LORD TERMINUS ON THE BENCH...

Next case be a moite fretty yür worship — zo Oi rackons—

What's the charge? ... *pushing a bus over?!* How's the fellow plead?

Aarr, thaat be trooble, zir — he don't talk Queen's English loike oos — Oi caan't even foind aot his name...

Disfella tikitboi bilong motoka i ologeta balatiful — kikim baksait bilong mi. Olrait, mi shovim motoka bilong im.

Any means of identification? — apart from the All Whimshire Tennis & Croquet Club sweater!...

This note were faond on 'im, zir — joost a name and address, loike—

Chumble, eh?... H'mm, I'll remand him in custody till we can get hold of the Rector and see if he knows anything...

AND SO:

Mr. Chumble, you say the accused Bilipuss is apparently the victim of circumstances in inadvertently taking a drug—

Something that could happen to *any* of us, your — um — worship—

— but if he can be released, Mrs Pinyon has volunteered to guarantee his — um — behaviour — and a number of my parishioners wish to subscribe his return fare to the — um — Wayward Isles — as a gesture to one of a different — um — colour..

Well, I understand the Bus Company are not anxious to prefer charges — not being keen to spread it around that one of their buses was pushed over with one hand... I think the accused could be bound over..

OUTSIDE THE COURTROOM...

THOUSE

Come on, Bilipuss, you'd better come home and change back into your clothes—

Yes, indeed!

AT COPSE COTTAGE, A SACRIFICE

A pity about this yumyum — it was my most successful brew..

A darned sight too successful —

Well — I'll just pop down to the Green Man and order a keg of their rough cider —

That won't be necessary — I cut a lot of nettles from Mulch's field — this time I'm making hock —

Well, if you think I'm going to go through the business of treading nettles in my bare feet you're jolly well —

That's all taken care of, Pinny —

Mi longtaim wokabout long bagarap gras bilong yufella, mekim gudfella terink olosem yumyum..?

AT THE RECTORY, THE REV. CHUMBLE IS HAVING A LITTLE CELEBRATION...

The Bishop of Quirk!..

It is — um — good of you to come, my lord —

Not at all, Chumble — tell me, how is the fabric fund..?

It is well past its target, thanks to all the — um — publicity — and my later appearances in Meeting Point and — um — Juke Box Jury..

M'yes... Of course, publicity is never without a measure of embarrassment —

Chumble, I have felt for some time that a man of your talents is rather wasted in this parish, and now that Canon Chasuble has retired from the benefice of St Ursula Upwinkle —

It is most kind of you, my lord, to speak of my — um — preferment —

but I feel that my place is here with my flock, and I should hate them to feel that their shepherd was being — um — taken away from them —

Mr. + Mrs. Pinyon and Mr. Bilipuss!

Heaven forfend, Chumble — pray forget that I spoke of this —

AND NOW A SEA STORY, FULL OF SCUDDING SPUME AND SCREAMING SQUALLS AND MESSING ABOUT IN BOATS...

GADFLY

GAD

OUTWARD HO!

STARRING COLONEL PEWTER, MARTIN, GLUB & OF COURSE CHLOE, AS SHIP'S CAT...

& FEATURING ALL KINDS OF ASSORTED NAUTICAL CHARACTERS.

1

OUR STORY BEGINS IN THE STUDY AT 'CHUKKAS', COL. PEWTER'S WHIMSHIRE HOME...

Excuse me, Uncle— Mrs Aspic says tea's ready —would you like it served in here or in—

Quiet, boy!

2

—I'm in the middle of a tricky bit of business—dashed tricky...

Oh—I'm sorry, Uncle, I should've noticed you were wearing your cosy—

Let's see now: Lat—how the devil did this marmalade get on to the scale? Latitude 50°33'N.

— that means we should be just about... here... Eh? That's rum...

There—you see..? Allowing for Thingumbob's Projection, this chart is exactly like the coast of Maine here—

Well... it is a bit...

Now then: take a look at the date on that Chart, lad—what does it say?

Um—fourteen ...thirty-two.

Exactly. And can you remember the date Columbus discovered America...?

Oh...'In—um—fourteen hundred and ninety-two, Columbus sailed the Ocean blue'...

Quite correct —or, hang on, wasn't it 'In 1493, Columbus sailed the Deep Blue Sea...'In 1494, Columbus sailed from shore to shore'—

Uncle, please! What does it all mean?

This can only mean one thing, boy: Columbus couldn't've discovered America because it had already been charted sixty years before...

Who by, Uncle?

Ah! There's a signature on that chart—Roger Squire, an old Whimshire sea-captain. This old manuscript tells us about him—it's a sort of poem—

There—rum lingo it's written in, but one gets the drift. Read it out, boy—

'This Shipman was ther, y'clepped Rogere Squyer, For aught I woot he was of Whilomshyre'—

'He was a verrey parfit marinee With hewe al broun and swich a glaringe yë. In Engoland his barge knewe everiche cryke, And eek hadde goon the Naunce to'—

That's it, boy—the last line gives the clue!

"And eek hadde goon the Naunce to Armorik'... There, what d'you make of that, boy?

I–I don't make anything of it, I'm afraid—

Why, allowing for the rotten spelling, it can only mean he sailed his ship the Nancy to America! He must've been the first to chart that stretch of coast!'...

Cribey! You mean—

I mean that America was not discovered by an Italian courtier in the pay of the Spaniards, but by a bluff British sea-dog—and a whimshire-man to boot!'...

I spose they did call it America before Columbus..?

And, what's more, I mean to see the world knows all about it, by Jingo!'...

9

What are you going to do, Uncle?—Send these old papers to the British Museum so's they can confirm what you say, and tell the whole world?

Stuff! lad, this is no job for landlubberish penpushers—

It needs a blue-water man with salt in his veins to put this to the test. We're going to show 'em with deeds, not words—

I'm going to see that honour falls where it is due, to the true discoverer of America—

We..? Golly, you don't mean—

And we're going to do it by sailing in the wake of the Nancy!'...

10

No time for rotting, Glub – we've got lots to do – and toot sweet!

Golly! When are we going then, Uncle?

Before the sun touches the yardarm – well, in a matter of days, anyway –

I'm having the *Gadfly* completely refitted at the Tawnyport yards. We'll have packing to do, and stores to stow, and fitting out and stuffing in, and general messing about, and then –

– it's Outward Ho! on the trail of the *Naunce* – and the honour of Britannia as the stakes!...

13

AND SO PREPARATIONS ARE MADE FOR THE VOYAGE TO 'ARMORIK' –...

Only **one** of those, Glub – our hold space is pretty tight, y'know –

THE COMMISSARIAT IS STOCKED...

Right: Gentlemen's Relish, Turtle meat, calipash, Bombay duck, smoked ox tongues, Wiltshire hams, game pies, plum duffs, Stilton, Bath Olivers, muffins, bloater paste, knife powder...

Seltzer...

AND THE GADFLY'S CREW HEADS FOR TAWNYPORT.

14

AT LAST GADFLY IS READY FOR HER TRIALS, AND IS THOROUGHLY PUT THROUGH HER PACES...

Right, Glub, we'll get under way — cast off!

Ay, ay, sir —

EXCITING COMMENT ALL THE WAY...

Aghshwsh!

17

Ha, she'll do! Goes like a bird, eh, chaps...?

THE SKIPPER IS WELL SATISFIED WITH THE TRIALS...

Time to turn in, chaps — we sail on the morning tide...

GADFLY

AND SO THE COMPANY SETTLE DOWN FOR THEIR LAST NIGHT IN PORT...

ROGER SQUIRE
DISCOVERER OF AMERICA

AND DAWN SEES GADFLY SLIP HER MOORINGS AND HEAD FOR THE OPEN SEA...

18

WE TAKE UP OUR NARRATIVE FROM THE GADFLY'S LOG...

'First day out: Got under way nicely apart from a tiresome brush with a coal-barge. Squire would've run the scum down...'

'Third day out: Everything going very smoothly. Really, the Gadfly seems to run itself...'

Glub: wind's getting up — nip up and reef the mains'l —

Ay, ay, sir

'Sixth day: Have run into thick belt of fog. Getting worse — I can hardly see to wri

'Ninth day: Fog lifted, thank goodness. Glorious weather. Pressing on under full canvas without a care —'

19

'12th day out: Got a sun shot. We appear to be bang on Roger Squire's course'...

Here's where we've come, look — along this line between this heraldic sea-creature and this wrecked galleon —

Oh, sir!

— And here's where we are now — where he's filled in a bit of space with this ridiculous old puffing sea-god —

Colonel Pewter, sir —!

20

What is it, Glub? — I'm dashed busy down below here in the chart-room —

Could you step on deck a moment, sir..?

— It looks a bit — nasty...

AND IN A TRICE *GADFLY* IS ENGULFED, BUT HER SKIPPER IS EQUAL TO THE CHALLENGE...

Heave to, Glub! Lash the helm! Haul in the mainsheet! Close the hatches! Man the pumps!

Oh, and *you*, boy — nip down to the hold and bring up a box of La España Perfectos —

Cigars, Uncle? — oh, ay ay, sir!

What are you doing, Uncle? — lightening ship..?

Just a sop to old Squire's sea-god, boy — won't do any harm —

BUT AS THEY GO BELOW TO RIDE OUT THE STORM IT SEEMS TO INCREASE IN ITS FURY:

Hmm — perhaps I should've made it Coronas...

CLUNK

21.

FOR FIVE WHOLE DAYS THE STORM RAGES. TO QUOTE THE LOG: "Wind Force 8. Lying a-hull under bare poles, thrown on beam ends by extra good one. Mast snapped'...

Boy! Bring me another plate of soup!...

'...Wind Force 9. Running dead before, streaming warps. Pitch-poled by pooping sea. Rudder gone'...

Steady as she go-o-o-oes!...

'Wind Force 10. Doghouse struck by lightning. After section flooded. Strums to pumps blocked. Jettisoned all gear aft and bailed'...

'Wind freshening, sea still lumpy. Beginning to look a bit sticky, actually — down to our last tin of Brasso'...

22

AT LAST THE STORM CLEARS, AND GADFLY'S CREW BEGIN TO DRY OUT — AND TO TOT UP THE DAMAGE:

Hmm — dismasted, rudderless, waterlogged, pumps jiggered, wireless kaput — and one of Mr Aspic's plum duffs came adrift and smashed through the bulkhead... But its not all loss, chaps —

— This wretched door that used to stick has eased nicely now... Well, to work, chaps —

FROM THE LOG AGAIN: 'Swell gone down. Rigged emergency steering'...

I say, do buck up, Glub — just winkle the bent pintle out of the gudgeon eye and straighten it —

Ugfgh..

GADFLY

23

...Fitted jury rigging. Replaced broken jib halyard with Thurston web braces. Now running under twill Ceylon lugs'l and flannel fores'l...

Ah, she'll soon pick up her skirts now, chaps...

'GADFLY becalmed under leaden skies. Making some progress under auxiliary power'...

...In — out — in — out — Come on, Glub — give it ten! One — two — three —

..'Ghosting to light air. Still no sun'...

Uncle, where are we now, exactly..?

Blest if I know, boy — we're off course, and no landmarks to be seen —

Y'know, those old time sailors in Roger Squire's day believed that when you got lost, dead men would bob up out of the sea to point the way —

They must've been simple jacktars all right — just imagine —

24

— Crikey!... Uncle — what's **that**?!

AND OFF GOES SIMO WITH GADFLY ON HIS TAIL:

Just as well we ran up a full canvas, Glub, or we'd never keep up with him...

33

UNTIL, AT LAST...

Land! Look, Uncle—up at the front, over there!

On the starb'd bow, boy, *if* you please....Jove, yes, just to the right of the sharp end!

Can't find it on the chart—could be any of these uninhabited dots...

Looks like a small inlet at one end—Simo's heading for it

We'll just about make harbour on the tide before dusk—Right, Glub, stow all sails down to your vest...

AND GADFLY RUNS SMOOTHLY INTO HARBOUR:

Good old Simo—he's leading us in—

Colonel—Isn't that a light over there?

Where?

34

Phosphorescence, I dare say—keep your eye on the pilot, Glub—

Over there—oh, it's gone now—

He's over here!

No, no—here he is on this quarter—

I see him, Sir—straight ahead—

He's over this side!

Oh...I see it now—there's more than one, by Jingo!..

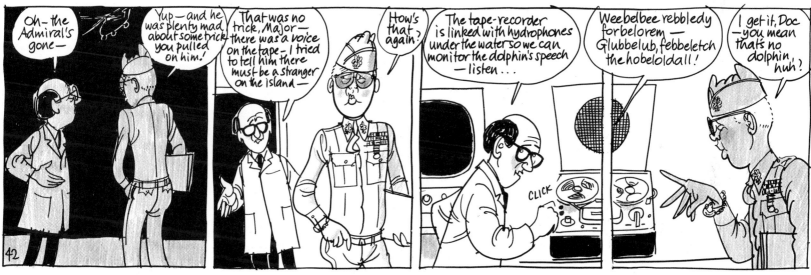

Hey! The screen's blank — they've shot out the floodlights!

It's damaged the hydrophones too — there's no sound...

45

Doc, this is war! We gotta get those lousy Reds!

Well, that net across the mouth of the inlet will keep their boat in — it works automatically

My men will be flying in at 0800 hours — I'll make up a boarding party then. I gotta work out a plan of attack. C'mon, Doc, I'll need local maps, black coffee...Cookies—

AND BACK IN THE INLET...

Well, that's stopped their little game for now. But I'll post guards tonight, chaps — you can bet they'll be back!

AT FIRST LIGHT, AFTER AN UNEVENTFUL NIGHT, GADFLY'S CREW TAKE TO THE DINGHY:

It's near high tide again — we'll take a look at that net—

46

Gad! It's higher than last night — they must have some way of raising it—

Hmm — too thick to cut — we could try blowing a hole in it—

But Uncle! That could kill some of the dolphins!

Well, we're not going to wait here like a sitting duck — one thing for it chaps: take to the hills!...

PRESENTLY:
What flag's she flying, Sergeant?

Can't see any, sir—except what looks like an undervest—

...Hmm—that's not in the flag-book— Can you see any name on her stern?

G-A-D-F-L-Y...

53

Gadfly, huh? Well, this Gadfly's gonna get stung— set up your bazooka and cover me, Sergeant—I want to parley—

Yes, sir

Ahoy! Gadfly—show yourself and state your business...

No—put a shot across their bows!

They're not answering, sir—

54

AND NEXT MOMENT—

WROOMPH!

BACK AT THE RESEARCH STATION:

Gunfire! I hope they're not hurting the dolphins...

AND UP ON THE HEIGHTS...

By Jingo! chaps—they're shooting at the Gadfly. Glub: load the cannon!

Um—what with, sir..?

AND BEFORE LONG...

... Analysis of the dolphin's speech patterns reveals a consistent — Oh dear...

'ROOOAR...'

Senator: this is Dr Pilstein, Director of Research — Senator Drumhead —

No Guard of Honour, Admiral? Where are all your men...?

59

Yes, where are my Marines, Doctor? Why isn't Major Maulschutzer here to meet us?

They're all over at the inlet Admiral — they're attacking a strange ship —

CRUMP!

I hate to think what's happening to the dolphins...

Let's get over there, Senator!

OVER AT THE INLET...

Keep up small arms fire at that enemy mortar position, men —

Yes, sir

Muldoon — stop eating that flak — take it easy, man!

...Exactly like Aunt Biddy's home-made cake...

Major — there's another lot sneaking up on us from the rear — I'll give 'em a burst, huh?

Hold it, Scarlatti —

60

Don't fire, you fool — its the Admiral!..

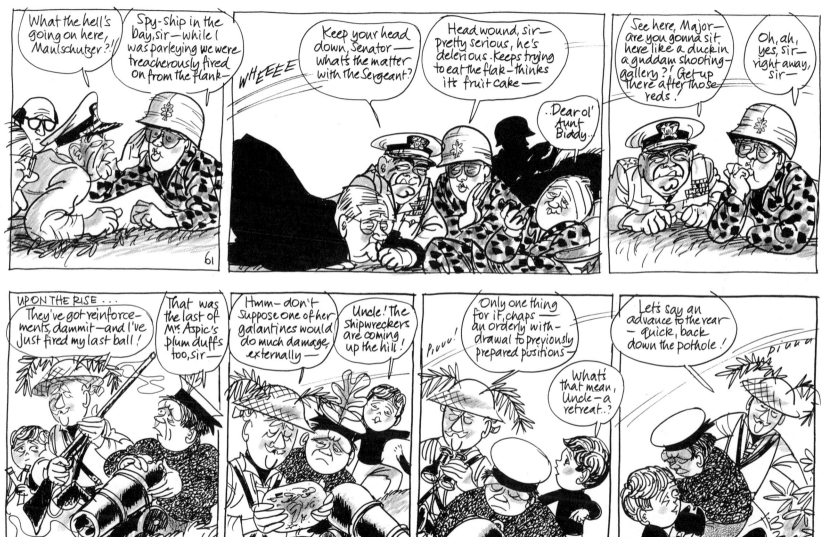

QUICKLY THE *GADFLY'S* DEFENDERS MAKE THEIR WAY BACK THROUGH THE POTHOLE...

UNTIL

Gad! What's this?

We can't go any further — the water's flooded in!

63

The dinghy will've sunk too!...

Jove! I wish I'd thought to look up my diary

—It says today's was a *neap* tide... Jolly good diaries these... Savonarola martyred, 1498...

GLONK!

Okay, Senator...?

Uncle! They're coming after us — they must've found the opening!

This is a bit of a poser, chaps — we're between the devil and the deep blue sea, as it were —

'N' the devil's getting awf'ly close...

CLONK

Right — we'll have to take to the drink, chaps — be sure to keep your powder dry —

Uncle, there's something coming up from the entrance to the cave —

It's Simo!...He's come to help us — and he's brought a friend —

Oh goody! It's Melusine!...

THE COLONEL STATES HIS TERMS...

You will cease messing us about, and allow us to effect repairs to our vessel and depart—

And let the dolphins out of the net, don't forget, Uncle—

69

Oh yes – arrange for the release of this prisoner and his friends–

Yes, yes – only get her to *stop!*

That will do very nicely, thanks... I say, old girl, *do pipe down* –

Oh... I usually do a short encore...

Guddammit, Senator, I musta been blown off my bridge – where's the enemy?

Never mind, Plumb – I've arranged a truce...

AND SO THE GADFLY'S CREW RETURN TO THE BOAT:

Gad! Now there's a noble sight, chaps...

70

Well, those wreckers don't seem to have done any damage. How's the Commissariat, Glub? – I'm jolly peckish –

You can have anything you like, sir – bar plumduff...

Oh well I think just some sheep's head broth... curried prawns... ham ramakins... kebobs... duck salmi — and treacle pudding to follow...

And a couple of tins of sardines—

– for our ESCORT...

PRESENTLY :

Look, Uncle — the net's down — the dolphins are leaving —

All except Simo—he's staying!

71

AND SURE ENOUGH THE DOLPHINS ARE LIGHTING OUT FOR THE OPEN SEA...

SOON, ON THE FAR SIDE OF THE ISLAND...

There they go, Miss Otis — the last of the dolphins — and the end of our research station...

But they are better off this way. One can only say : 'Nyek hek nuh kek hek'.*

Nyek, hyekek.**

* Good-bye, dolphins   ** Good luck...

MELUSINE'S VICTIMS HAVE CHANGED INTO DRY CLOTHES...

Admiral, I'm sorry I couldn't find you anything to fit you better—

Forget it, Major — these will do till I get back to my ship—

72

Well, Pilstein, your porpoises have flown — this is the end of your research station—

And of the SPUT Project, no doubt

Yup — to be frank, I thought it was a pretty lousy idea, myself — but it was that or Operation Overload — using my planes to drop bedbugs behind the enemy lines —

Admiral, can you get me back to your ship, raght away?

Right away, Senator — well, I guess this is bit of a blow, huh?, losing your brain-child—

Hunh..? Oh, *that* — that's old stuff, Plumb — Ah've got a brand noo ahdeah...

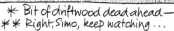

AND NOW, AS SPRING IS USHERED IN WITH THE CLICKING OF THE FIRST TURNSTILE, WE PRESENT—

SPECIAL ATTRACTION

A STORY OF STATELY HOMES AND BROODY HENS, AND SOMETHING RATHER NOVEL AT CROMBLEIGH PARJIT.

Starring Lord ('Jumbo') TERMINUS and introducing MRS DINWIDDIE.

STABLES ORANGERY HA-HA TOILETS ←

FOLLY CAR PARK GAZEBO GROTTO ←

OUR STORY BEGINS IN COLONEL PEWTER'S WHIMSHIRE HOME, ROUND ABOUT NOW...

Oh, Glub: I want the de Gupy—bring it round, will you?

Yes, sir— I'll just change into my uniform—

That won't be necessary—I'm just running over to Crombleigh Parjit, I'll drive myself—

Yes, sir— oh, before you go, sir —Mrs Aspic wants me to kill a boiler for her. Which one can I take?

Oh... that last broody old Rhode Island-Whimshire cross—hasn't laid for ages—she'll do—

Very good, sir —I'll get the motor now...

AT THIS MOMENT, DOWN IN THE FOWLYARD...

Chloe! Stop that!.

ARK-KUK!

MEANWHILE COLONEL PEWTER IS PAYING A VISIT TO CROMBLEIGH PARJIT, SEAT OF LORD TERMINUS...

Hello there, Pewter — Scotch..?

I see your chaps are hard at it licking the old place into shape for the Season —

M'yes — can't say the prospects are any too bright —

Had a pretty poor season last year — didn't even pay for the keep of the death-watch beetle...

I say, hard cheese.

My dear chap, what you need to rake in the half-crowns is a thing-ummy — you know, a special attraction —

Mmp..?

M'yes — a special attraction — that's the ticket!

Dammit, man, we've got bags of 'em — there's the gazebo — the ha-ha — the priest-hole — and Molly's stall where she sells jars of calf's foot jelly made from her own calves —

Then there's the Hermit in the Grotto — although last year's was a bit off — we lost our regular chap, he left to get a job in the local supermarket —

We had to make do with a couple of school leavers on alternate days — not very successful, I'm afraid...

It's a funny thing, the public just don't seem to go for a beardless hermit —

Particularly when he insists on playing his transistor all day long...

MEANWHILE, BACK AT 'CHUKKAS'...

Please Mr Glub — not Mrs Dinwiddie!

AND SO—NOT WITHOUT INCIDENT—THE DRAGON IS TRANSPORTED TO CROMBLEIGH PARUIT...

Aarr, doanee vret, Becky, 'tes nabbut zoom nü-vungled goind uv cao, Oi rackon—

AND DULY INSTALLED IN THE GROTTO...

Phew! That's got him behind bars at last—

Well, thanks for all your help, Colonel—I'm sure he'll be a great success—

Good luck, old man—and take care: dragons can be tricky, y'know...

DRAGON

LATER...

Well, old girl, tomorrow will see a change in our fortunes—it's D-for-Dragon Day!

D for Doomsday, I'd say...

32

AND SO COMES D-FOR-DRAGON DAY...

Ye gods! There's a great queue of coaches—and we don't open for an hour!

33

AND WHEN THE GATES ARE OPENED...

Hey! Where's the dragon then?!

Where's the dragon?

Aarr—where be draagon?

Bitte, wo ist der Drache?

NOR IS MERVYN FOUND WANTING...

Inny fierce?!

Look at the smoke!

Most convincing—plastic of course.

Very clever...

AND AT THE END OF THE DAY...

What did I tell you?—It's the best day we've ever had since we threw Crombleigh open!

It's early days yet...

AND BEFORE LONG LORD TERMINUS'S DRAGON HAS HAD SOME GRATIFYING PUBLICITY — FROM THE LOCAL PRESS...

Come along, young Catchpole — haven't you finished that piece about the local dragon yet?

I'm having to do it from scratch, s.p.,— I got a bit close and my notebook went up in flames!

Whimshi Clarion

FROM FLEET STREET...

...Today, for the first time since the days of King Arthur, a man stood face to face with a fierce, fire-breathing dragon... I was reminded of a time in the second world war when I felt the hot blast of burning oil-wells in far-off Borneo...

34

FROM THE TELEVISION SCREEN...

Without having examined this creature, one can point out that modern zoology recognizes twenty species of the genus *Draco*, or flying lizard, belonging to the family *Agamidae*. The possibility of a mutation...

AND EVEN FROM ABROAD...

DIE WELT

In England: Erst der Minirock dann der Minidrache

France-Soir

EN ANGLETERRE: ENCORE UN DRAGON POUR TONY ET MARGARET? On dit que c'est de rigueur pour toutes les "Stately Homes"

The New York Times

British Dragon not Red China Import, Wilson tells LBJ

AFTER A FEW WEEKS...

Well, Terminus: how's the Special Attraction?

GROTTO

Oh, hello Pewter! Going like a bomb — getting bigger and fiercer every day!

Knocks young Montagu's old cars into a cocked hat... Chatsworth'll be feeling the draught too, I expect—

Ah, nothing like a spot of Big Game

I'm a bit worried about Bath, though — he's got about fifty lions and he's breeding from them — d'you think I should increase my stock?

Breed dragons, you mean?— worth a shot, I dare say—

Tell you what: I'll wire my Indian chappie to rush another clutch of eggs over—

Jolly good, Colonel-please do that...

DANGER THIS ANIM BREAT FIRE

35

Courage? Why should it need courage to show a dragon?

You're not afraid of history repeating itself?

What history?

The Saga of the Dragon of Whimshire. It is recounted by the old Whimshire poet Wynkyn Yog—

I just happen to have a copy of his book in my bag—perhaps I could read it to you—

Please don't bother, Mr. Pin—

AND SO MRS. PINYON BEGINS...

Whylom ther was dwellinge in Whylomshire A dragon fiers which belched smok & fyr...

MRS. PINYON CONTINUES THE SAGA OF THE DRAGON OF WHIMSHIRE...

Thilk laidly wyrm wer grisly to bΘholde,
Ten yerdès longe with limes grete & bolde;
Up-on his shuldres wingès hadde he tweyne,
His bodie covered was lyk armure-cheyne;
The circles of the eyen in his heed,
They gloweden betwixe yelow & reed.
Eek everich day this dragon swalwed doun
A wench fro oon or other contree toun,
Till peple gan to fere eftsoons moot be
Na wenches left to stert a familie.

Atte laste bifel to face this fate moost dyre
The doghter of the King of Whylomshire.

47

Anon ther cam up-on the scene
A gentil knighte y'cleppèd Galantine;
Tall as an asshe up-on his foomy stede
'I trowe,' quod he, 'this dragon moot be deed.'
And in the wood at tyme & place y-set,
Thilk dragon & thilk Galantine ben met.

Sodenliche the knighte pulled out his swerd,
The dragon spronge lyk cat up-on a byrd;
And in this wyse togidre thurgh the wood
Up to the ancle foghte they in hir blood.

Atte laste the knighte made swich a mighty [bounde
And smoot the dragones heed eek to the grounde.

A grateful fader offered the knighte
The hande of her he saved fro swich plyte
'I trowe,' quod he, 'I fayner wolde instede
That I coude carrye hoom the dragones heed'...

MRS PINYON PAUSES IN HER RECITAL OF WYNKYN YOG...

Of course that's just the prologue: the Tale itself goes on to —

Some other time, Mr Pinyon, if you would —

You're not afraid of **your** dragon getting out and terrorising the county?

I should think we could still cope in this day and age — there's the Ministry of Agriculture chaps for a start —

Then there's the Whimshire Constabulary.. the Territorials, or whatever.. and we could always call on a detachment of the Duffs as a last resort —

Poor dragon! Let's hope it won't come to that... Well, good luck!

Fool of a woman! — making an excuse to come here and spout all that old rubbish about knights rescuing damsels in distress —!

Hmm, you might be glad of one yourself one day...

48

OVER AT 'CHUKKAS'...

Uncle, I'm a bit worried about Mrs Dinwiddie —

Not laying, you mean? She hardly ever does — ought to've got rid of her ages ago —

It's not that — she's sort of — moping...

Let's have a look at her, hmm?

I think she's missing Mervyn! — she was very attached to him, really.

Oh, she'll get over it — the chicks have got to leave the nest you know...

WHILE, OVER AT CROMBLEIGH PARK IT...

What is it, Mellors?

It's the dragon, sir — I don't like the look of him....

A HISTORY OF ~SHIRE VOL. I

49

AND A FEW DAYS LATER...

Councillor Niggle, my lord...

Ha! Niggle: what the devil is this letter of yours all about?

I should have thought it explained itself: it is a Schedule of Modifications which as Chairman of the Fire Committee—

I can see all that, man, —but why pick on me?

Following the Fire Officer's Report on fire hazards this list of items was drawn up to assess what is required to make your grotto conform to Fire Regulations for Places of Entertainment—

Emergency exit... asbestos curtain—hang it all, Niggle, you never insisted on this nonsense when we showed our hermit in the grotto!

Well, no: but then you never had a hermit who breathed on the Inspector's back and burnt a hole in his plastic mac...

52

Hang it all, Niggle, to do all these things would cost a fortune—I'll have to think about this—

That is entirely up to you, lord Terminus—

But if you wish to continue showing your dragon we must insist on the schedule being carried out to the letter. Goodday to you...

Wasn't that that Councillor Niggle I caught a glimpse of just now?

Yes—lot of red tape about fire regulations—someone must've put 'em on to me—

Chumble! By George! yes—I'll bet he was the nigger in the woodpile—and I'll jolly well find out!...

53

IN THE DRAWING ROOM...

Some man wanted to see you about the dragon — an official of some sort —

I saw him all right — sent him off with a flea in his ear —

I've also managed to upset old Hellfire Chumble and insult that self-appointed troubadour Mr Pinyon — this dragon business is getting me down...

This dam' beast was supposed to save our bacon, but if the Council have their way he'll see us in Queer St! Anyway, he's got the sulks and he's not even putting on a decent show. I'd get rid of him if I knew how!...

BUT THE SOLUTION TO LORD TERMINUS'S PROBLEM IS NO FURTHER AWAY IN SPACE & TIME THAN HIS OWN GROTTO AT THIS VERY MOMENT...

This is the joint I cased, Torchy — how d'you like the set-up..?

56

I don't get it, Moosh — you mean this thing is the loot..?

Pussy!

A very nice little property — and safe as houses —

Observe that fiery breath — now then, supposing this animal burns its way through the bars in the night and out the door —

But you'd need a blow-torch for —

Well, they look for it locally for a bit — and then give it up as a dead loss — reckon it's crawled into a cave somewhere and snuffed it — right..?

Yeah — but where do we come in on this?

Well — Suppose another dragon turns up at a Stately Home up north — very like this one, but a different colour, and with different accessories —

A repaint! Now I get it!...

57

74

Mrs Pinyon, this is Superintendent Snagge, who's in charge of the missing dragon case—

Ah, I'm glad you're here, Superintendent—you'll be interested to hear my theory on where Lord Terminus's dragon is hiding—

I can hardly wait, Madam

It's all here in this splendid book by the old Whimshire poet Wynkyn Yog—you remember my reading you the Prologue, Lord Terminus—

Vividly—but please don't put yourself to the—

I have marked the pertinent passage which I think gives a definite clue to the dragon's whereabouts—

Can I see it?

The language is rather difficult—I think it would be clearer if I read it out...

Oh, very well.

ONCE MORE FABIA PINYON BRINGS TO LIFE THE WORDS OF WYNKYN YOG...

Thilke dragon werd dwellinge undergrounde,
In swich darke caverne he coulde nat ben faunde;
His paleys hadde of chambres a ful score,
And everich oon oped on to severall more;
Decked thurgh-out with pyles of precious stoons,
And filled oon by oon with maydenes boons;
Til atte this tyme the dragon hadde to kepe
Oon chambre left wherein to eat & sleepe.

'I trowe, quod he, 'that I shol meet my doom
Thurgh eating my-selve out of hous & hoom'...

Ugh!.. Well..?

Don't you see? He describes the lair used by a 13th century dragon: its more than likely your dragon has chosen the same place—all we have to do is find it!

But— the only caves in Whimshire are up in the High Dudgeons—miles away from anywhere Mervyn's been spotted—

Hang on, sir—I've just thought of something—can I see your map again?

MEANWHILE, IN A DARK CAVERN NOT AWFULLY FAR AWAY...

75

'Pyles of precious stoons'— could be stalagmites. There's a string of underground limestone caves just about here — ah yes, they're marked on the map here, look—

They run from Wych Wood through to the High Street — about twenty of them. They were sealed off when the Council Chambers were built—

Quirk Council Chambers — so I was right!

And so was I, Colonel: `It is paleys hadde of chambres a ful score'...

Hmf — a bit far-fetched, I'd say...

Well, it's worth investigating — would you gentlemen care to come along?

Of course.

And me!

Ra-ther!

AND THE INVESTIGATING PARTY MOVE TO THE CAVES...

This is the entrance to the caves — it's got a bit grown over over the years ...

I say! these bushes have been trampled about, look!...

Hmm — it's a bit of a squeeze getting in... Bogg, you'd better try it—

Rroight, зirr...

...What's up, Bogg?... Can you see anything..?

Aarr...＊!!⁙＊†!!

'T'were a moight daarrk, зirr — boot Oi aave rreason tü believe the drraagon were prresent—

Imprinting..? Oedipus..? What the devil's all *that* got to do with getting my dragon out of a hole?!

Don't you see? All that needs to be done is for Mrs Dinwiddie to be dropped into the cave — she will then lead the dragon out —

Hmm — sounds to me like a cock-&-bull story...

A decoy, eh? Well, I don't know — I daresay it's worth a try —

If she can only get him to stick his head out, the Duffs will soon blast it off!

All right: I'll make the necessary arrangements. Will you lay on the hen, Colonel?

Eh?..oh, right — oh — I'll speak to the lad.

Oh, one thing: I wouldn't say anything to him about the Duffs...

Ah, there you are, lad. We've been discussing a little something *you* can do for us —

What is it, Uncle? You were a long time —

We want to borrow that hen of yours. She can help us get the dragon out of the cave —

How's that, Uncle?

Just a little wheeze of mine: I thought if your hen went into the cave and you called her out, she'd be bound to lead Merlin out as well!

Golly! That's a great idea —

That way Mervyn can be recaptured without getting hurt!

Why — ah — yes, that's the ticket! Well, that's fixed then...